Gwynedd Isaac

To Gwynedd
with best wishes for a very
Happy Christmas 1959.
From Uncle Bill Auntie Thelma

QUEEN OF SCOTS

# Queen of Scots

THE STORY OF MARY STUART

BY ELISABETH KYLE

*Illustrated by Robert Hodgson*

THOMAS NELSON AND SONS LTD EDINBURGH

THOMAS NELSON AND SONS LTD
Parkside Works Edinburgh 9
36 Park Street London W1
312 Flinders Street Melbourne C1
302–304 Barclays Bank Building
Commissioner and Kruis Streets
Johannesburg

THOMAS NELSON AND SONS (CANADA) LTD
91–93 Wellington Street West Toronto 1

THOMAS NELSON AND SONS
19 East 47th Street New York 17

SOCIÉTÉ FRANÇAISE D'EDITIONS NELSON
25 rue Henri Barbusse Paris V^e^

---

*First published 1957*

TO
MARY MACLIN GUÉRARD

Printed in Great Britain by
Thomas Nelson and Sons Ltd, Edinburgh

# I

ONE day long ago, four little girls were playing in a garden, in the middle of an island in Scotland. They all shared the same name, Mary, but as they were not sisters that didn't matter.

They were throwing a ball about, and the ball sometimes bounced over the hedge, so that they had to leave the garden to find it. Then they could see the grey waters of the lake which kept them prisoners on the island itself. But it kept them safe as well. For there was trouble and fighting in Scotland.

There was a fifth little girl, Mary Stuart, but she was not

in the garden. ' Why doesn't she come out and play ? ' asked Mary Beaton, throwing the ball.

' She's talking to her mother about something special,' said Mary Seton, catching the ball and adding, ' I hope she'll tell us what the special thing is——'

' Look ! She's coming ! ' Mary Fleming called out.

And there she was. She came running down the little path between the hedges, looking excited. She was the same age as the other Maries, but taller because her mother and father had been very tall people. She was the prettiest too, with red-gold hair, and eyes that changed colour so that nobody was quite sure just what colour they were.

And though she was only a little girl, she was more important than the other four, because she was a Queen. Her father King James V had died when she was a baby, and she had been crowned Queen of Scotland when she was one week old.

' Listen ! ' she cried, running up to them. ' What do you think ? We're going away from the Island ! '

' Where to ? ' the other four Maries said, all together.

' To France ! To my uncle, the King of France ! '

They gasped and looked at each other. France was so far away from Scotland. Mary Stuart enjoyed watching their surprised faces. She didn't ask if they wanted to go to France. She hadn't been asked herself. But wherever she went, the four other Maries must go too. They were her ladies-in-waiting. It was their duty to stay with her, always.

'My mother is frightened to keep me here any longer,' she explained. 'She thinks my uncle, the King of England, might march his soldiers into Scotland and take me away to London. He wants me to marry his son. Mother wants me to marry my French cousin instead, when I grow up. So we are going to France in a big ship, and we'll live in a splendid palace instead of an island——'

'Will we have to talk French?' asked Mary Livingstone rather crossly.

'I suppose we will,' Mary Stuart answered, 'but I can already, because my mother is French. Anyway, the servants are packing our things, so let's get back and see that they don't forget our favourite toys.'

When they got back to the house, there was great bustle going on. Their clothes, their

school-books, everything the little girls had, were being hurriedly packed into big wooden boxes. The boxes were ferried across the Lake, and the Maries with them. Almost before they realised what was happening they had landed, and ridden on their little ponies to where, in harbour, lay the big ship which was to take them over to France.

There, on the pier, stood some of the Scots Nobles to see Mary Stuart off. They were grim and quiet, and they carried swords in their hands. Mary's tall French mother, the Widow-Queen, was there too. She kissed her little girl goodbye, not knowing if she would ever see her again. But

Mary Stuart was so excited about going to France, that she didn't think of that.

So the great ship sailed away, with all her sails set. Scotland was left behind. But while the five Maries laughed and ran about the deck, a sailor kept watch, always, for any sign of an English ship coming after them. King Henry of England was going to be very angry when he heard that his son's bride had escaped !

However, they reached France quite safely. The King of France called Mary Stuart his little daughter, and gave her everything she wished. She and her four Maries had splendid toys to play with, and splendid rooms in splendid palaces to live in. They moved with the French Court, from the Palace in the middle of the forest, to the Palace with the great marble staircase and the peacocks screaming and spreading their tails in the gardens below ; or to the one where the fountains played all day.

The palaces had beautiful gardens, stretching for miles and miles. They were scented with roses, and watered by little streams, and jets of water which sprang like feathers into the air. Mary Stuart had dresses of silk and velvet, and so had the other Maries. Soon, the poor little garden on the island was almost forgotten. And even Mary Livingstone learned to speak French.

They learned other things too. Mary Stuart was clever. She learned Latin and Spanish, as well as writing and making up poetry, which was the fashion at Court. She wrote some very good poetry, and she sang and danced well. She learned to sew very finely, for that is a special art of the French. But she liked best to ride out into the great forest with her uncle the King, and hunt the deer. And every year she grew taller and prettier.

She had someone new to play with as well. Her cousin Francis, who was to marry her when she grew up, was a delicate, rather dull boy, and Mary was very kind to him because she was sorry for him.

' Must we take him with us ? ' Mary Seton complained. ' You know he always gets tired first, or gets hot or something. And his mother, Queen Catherine, makes such a fuss ! '

' Poor Francis ! ' Mary Stuart said. ' He can't help being delicate. I mean to be kind to him all my life.'

Perhaps the Queen of France was jealous because her son was so fond of Mary. Perhaps she was angry because Mary was pretty and gay. She herself was ugly and dark, and people even whispered that she used poisons to get her enemies out of the way. Anyhow, she hated the girl-queen from over the seas.

' Be careful,' warned Mary Fleming, the one whom Mary Stuart loved best of the four.

But Mary Stuart just laughed. ' My uncle the King will protect me,' she said, ' and when Francis becomes King, he will protect me too.'

Mary was sixteen now. Soon her wedding day arrived, and everyone said they had never seen so beautiful a bride. Her wedding dress was white. Her long velvet train was silver-grey, embroidered with pearls. The four Maries were her train-bearers, and a band of musicians arrived, all the way from Scotland, to make music at her wedding ball.

The fountains in the streets spouted wine. The fountains in the royal gardens played all night. All night long the people danced and feasted, and the strange foreign musicians from her own little country of Scotland played their queer music, which made the French people laugh.

Mary was very happy, and kind to her poor young husband. She had hardly time to spare a thought for Scotland, so far away. She need not be afraid any more of her English uncle, King Henry, who had died. She knew that his daughter, Elizabeth, was Queen in her own right, just as she herself was a Queen. She thought, as they were cousins, they should meet one day and be friends.

Her only grief was when news came that her mother had died far away in Scotland. But she scarcely remembered her. The Scots Nobles could still rule the country for her. Her place was with her husband in France. The sun shone so warmly there, and everyone (except the old queen, her mother-in-law) was kind and pleasant.

Then her uncle, the King of France, died too. Francis was King now, and Mary was the Queen of France. Queen

of France as well as of Scotland. And she couldn't help remembering that her cousin, Queen Elizabeth of England, was not married and was much older than she, and that she was her nearest relation.

Perhaps when Elizabeth died Mary would some day be Queen of England too !

# 2

BUT every day Francis, her boy-husband, grew weaker until he died. According to royal French fashions in mourning, Mary had to shut herself up in her own room for forty days, with her curtains drawn and only candles for light, by day as well as by night. She missed her gentle companion, and cried very much. And she dressed herself in white mourning instead of black. She wore a long white brocade gown, with a floating white veil. When people saw her again, they called her The White Queen.

When she began to go out again, everything in the palace was changed. She no longer reigned over France with her husband ; his brother was King now. People did not pay her the same respect. And the old Queen Catherine, her mother-in-law who had always hated her, now took the first place in the land.

' She even pushes me aside and enters a room before me ! ' Mary Stuart complained bitterly to Mary Fleming.

' Dear Madam, what does that matter ? ' Her friend tried to soothe her. ' At least your Majesty is still Queen of Scotland ! '

' Yes, so I am ! ' She dried her tears suddenly. ' Sooner

than stay here to be injured by that cruel woman, I shall go back to my own country. And you, my four Maries, will come with me too ! '

So it was arranged. A ship was ordered to be fitted out, and messages sent to Scotland to say that the Queen, who had gone away as a little girl, was now coming back to rule.

But when the time grew near to take ship, all the Maries grew sad. They could scarcely remember anything about Scotland, except the garden on the island where they used to play. Mary Stuart remembered that it was a very little garden, nothing like the beautiful ones in France. And the sun had not shone nearly so brightly in Scotland. But at least she would be a Queen there, and do what she liked !

So she chose beautiful silks and velvets to take with her, and perfumes that smelt of all the flowers of France ; and even one or two of the tiny dogs that ran, yapping, down the long corridors of the French palaces, for Mary loved dogs. Then she said goodbye to all her friends, and embarked on the ship with her Maries.

The great sails were spread and the ship glided out of the harbour. All day Mary Stuart stayed on deck, watching the coast-line fade behind her. When night came, she had a bed made up on deck and slept there. But she asked the sailor on watch to promise that, when dawn came if France was still visible, he would wake her to see the last of it.

The wind dropped in the night and the ship scarcely

moved. So when the sky and water turned pink in the morning light, she could still just see a faint line, like a thread, which stood for the land where she had been so happy. She

stretched out her arms to it and said, 'Goodbye, France, goodbye! I shall never see thee again!'

After a few days (for ships moved very slowly under sail) they drew near to the coast of Scotland. The air had turned colder, and they landed at the port of Leith, near Edinburgh, in a thick fog. There was no wireless or telegraph in those days, so nobody expected them. Instead of being greeted with music and courtiers and flowers and rejoicing, as she had always been in France, poor Mary stepped ashore with no-one to welcome her at all !

However, the Scots Lords rode hastily out from Edinburgh, led by Mary's half-brother Lord Moray who had been looking after the country during her absence. They escorted her to her capital, and as soon as the Edinburgh people heard that their Queen was really back among them, they crowded under the windows of her palace of Holyrood House to welcome her.

It was a poor little palace, compared with the splendid ones in which she had lived in France. The wind blew down the long stone corridors, and the rooms were small and dark. But Mary was determined to make the best of things and be as happy as she could. She gave balls and parties. She invited musicians to her Court, and she and the other Maries amused themselves by dressing up and playing tricks on people. When she rode out into the city the people cheered her, she was so pretty and friendly, and they were pleased to have their Queen back again after so many years.

One person was not pleased with her, however. That man was John Knox, the leader of the Presbyterian Church. While Mary was away in France, matters had become worse and worse between the Catholics of ' the old religion ' as they called it, and the Protestants who now ruled Scotland.

Old John Knox was like a lion, defending the Protestant faith. He knew Mary was a Catholic like her French mother, and that she had been brought up in a Catholic country. He was afraid she might help to turn Scotland Catholic again, and he was sorry that she was so popular with her people.

'They come around her like bees round the honey-pot!' he complained.

So Mary had her troubles, because the Protestant Nobles were suspicious of her too. They quarrelled among themselves and each tried to grab power from the other. They were specially jealous of Mary's secretary, an ugly Italian called David Rizzio, whom they called 'Seigneur Davey'.

He had one twisted shoulder, but was very clever and gay. He was also honest, and he gave the Queen good advice. Perhaps she liked that. Perhaps even better she liked the songs he sang. Seigneur Davey sang and played beautifully.

He could sing the songs she had heard in France, and play the sparkling Italian tunes she liked to dance to. So she always had him near her.

Mary Fleming warned her again. ‘ Be careful,’ she said : ‘ your Majesty’s Nobles are becoming jealous ! ’

But Mary Stuart just laughed. ‘ Jealous of a poor twisted creature like Davey ? In any case, I am the Queen. I shall have him to sing and play to me as much as I like.’

So she went on, filling her little Scots palace with laughter and song ; giving great banquets to her Nobles and trying to win their friendship, and getting fine furniture sent over from France to make her rooms look more like a Queen’s.

Princes from overseas wanted to marry her, but she could not make up her mind. Sometimes she wrote to her cousin,

Queen Elizabeth of England, for advice. She did this more to compliment and flatter the Queen of England than anything else, because if she ever married again, she meant to marry whom she liked.

Both Queens were filled with curiosity to know what the other was like. Neither could leave her kingdom to visit the other, though they pretended that they would love to do so. But they were secretly a little afraid of each other.

Elizabeth was afraid, because Mary was a Catholic, and the Catholics in England would have liked to make her their queen. And Mary knew that Elizabeth's country was far richer and more powerful than hers. So, for fear of offending Elizabeth, Mary did not choose anyone else to marry for a long while.

Her four Maries were sorry for this. One or two of them wanted to get married themselves. But they had all made a promise that none would choose a husband until she did. Mary remembered this when she gave a great Feast on Twelfth Night. The banqueting hall was a blaze of candles and everyone was splendidly dressed. The Queen's Maries looked almost as beautiful as she did, and before they went in to supper, she called them aside.

'I'm going to release you from your promise,' she said, 'you may marry as soon as you like.'

The chief dish was a huge cake with a bean hidden inside it. Whoever got a slice with the bean in it was to rule the party for that night. Everyone was delighted when gentle Mary Fleming, the Queen's favourite, held up the bean.

Mary Stuart clapped her hands. ' If you are queen instead of me, you must wear my robes and my crown ! Come, we shall go and change dresses.'

When they came back hand in hand, everyone gasped. For the Queen of Scots was now dressed in plain black and white without a single jewel, except a diamond ring which she wore on a chain round her neck. But Mary Fleming was splendid in scarlet and gold, and she wore her mistress's golden crown.

Mary Stuart curtseyed to her mockingly. ' How does your Majesty wish us to amuse ourselves ? ' she asked.

Mary Fleming said that she wished to dance. So the court musicians struck up, and the dance began, sending music down the desolate passages of the palace which had been empty so long. The people of Edinburgh saw the palace windows lit up and knew that their queen was enjoying herself. They did not know that someone else was wearing her crown and giving orders, just for the night.

As Mary Stuart's little feet pointed and tapped down the dance, her partner asked why she wore that one jewel and no other ?

' This ring ? ' She fingered it with her free hand as it hung from her neck. ' I am wearing it because it is a present from my cousin the Queen of England. Her Ambassador is here, perhaps he will tell her I have paid her that compliment.'

'It has a beautiful diamond.' The Scots Noble watched how fire blazed from it in the bright candlelight.

Mary smiled. 'My cousin Elizabeth told me that if I was ever in danger, or needed help, I had only to send this ring to her and she would help me at once. But what help would I need from her?'

# 3

It was a fine day, and the gardens round Queen Elizabeth's palace outside London lay scented in sunshine. High clipped hedges cast shadows across their paths. The Scottish Ambassador, Sir James Melville, stood anxiously watching one of the paths. He had been told that the English Queen would come down it to speak to him. What sort of a woman was this Queen, who ruled in her own right as his Queen Mary did?

Round the side of the hedge she came. Her skirts were spread so wide, they reminded him of a ship in full sail. She was glittering with jewels as she walked proudly toward him. She had very little hands and feet, but not so pretty a face as Mary's. It was a thin, clever face, turned sharply toward him.

He bowed very low. She gave him her hand to kiss. 'You are from my dear cousin, Mary the Queen of Scots? Tell her I have her picture always with me, and look at it often,' she told him graciously.

He bowed again, wondering if she meant what she said. The next moment she asked, 'What colour is your Queen's hair? Is her colour the best or mine? Which of us is the fairest? Tell me honestly.'

' Madam,' said the Ambassador, ' each Queen is the fairest in her own country.'

Elizabeth stamped her foot. ' I told you to tell me the truth ! ' she ordered.

The Ambassador stole a look at Elizabeth's red, curly hair and her long white face. He must not offend her, but he must tell the truth as well. ' Your Majesty has the whitest skin,' he said, ' but my Queen is very lovesome.'

' How tall is she ? ' snapped Elizabeth.

' Taller than your Majesty. She is very tall.'

Elizabeth looked pleased. ' She is too tall for a woman. My height is just right. Is she musical ? Does she play well ? '

Again the Ambassador had to be careful. So he replied : ' Reasonably, for a Queen.'

Then Elizabeth asked if Mary was going to marry anyone, and the Ambassador, knowing that the English Queen had objected to every Prince who had come forward, became very cautious indeed. Elizabeth smiled again. ' I suppose you would like her to marry yon long lad ? ' she asked, pointing to the young Noble who stood just behind her, carrying the Sword of State.

Sir James looked at him. He was a very tall boy called Lord Darnley, and he was a cousin of both the Queens. He stood simpering in his silks and satins, like a conceited peacock. Sir James shook his head at once.

‘ No, I wouldn’t, Madam,’ he said bluntly. ‘ Lord Darnley looks just like a girl, for all he is so handsome.’

Then the Queen dismissed him and sailed on down the grassy walk, like a magnificent peacock herself. So the Ambassador went back to Scotland, and told Queen Mary everything her cousin had said.

‘ What right has she to say whom I am to marry or not to marry ? ’ Mary asked indignantly. Presently a thoughtful look came over her face. ‘ This Lord Darnley, you say he is tall and good-looking ? I would rather like to see him. . . .’

So Lord Darnley was invited to pay a visit to the Scottish Court. Not only was he handsome, he was a very good dancer, and Mary did not often find a man tall enough to partner her in the dances at the palace. Presently she fell in love with him and, to the dismay of her friends, announced that she was going to marry him.

They were married in the chapel one Sunday, and Lord Darnley put three wedding rings on her finger, to make everything sure. Three heralds blew on their trumpets and proclaimed Darnley King. But nobody cheered him at all, except his father who cried out, ‘ God save his Grace ! ’

At first they were happy. Mary did everything to please her husband and gave him everything he wanted. But as he was so stupid and conceited, his head began to swell to twice the size of a crown. He was rude to the great Nobles of the court, and to the servants. And soon he began trying to give Mary orders, and to interfere with the ruling of the country.

But he could not do that yet, for he was only a King in name. Mary was still the sovereign, and the more she saw of his silly behaviour, the more she determined not to let him have any power at all.

'Make me a real King!' he stormed at her. 'Order everyone to obey me as well as you!'

But Mary shook her head sadly. Once she had loved him, but now he only grieved and disappointed her. He had fallen in with a band of young men as bad and stupid as himself, and he spent all his days and nights feasting and drinking wine. How could she let a man like that help to govern her country?

The Scots Nobles, too, hated him more and more. Some of them began to think how they might get rid of him. They even planned to get rid of the Queen too, because they wanted the old days back, when she was safely in France and they could do as they liked.

So they hatched a plot. They were also jealous of the Italian, David Rizzio. Perhaps with luck, he could be got rid of, as well. . . .

'Look how near Seigneur Davey stands to the Queen's throne!' one of the Nobles in the plot would whisper into Darnley's jealous ear. 'He gives the Queen advice and she takes it. Yet she won't take it from you!'

‘Yes,’ whispered another, ‘perhaps it was Davey who advised her not to make you a real King ! No doubt he is afraid to let power slip from his hand to yours ! ’

‘If it’s true,’ Darnley muttered, clutching his sword, ‘I’ll kill the foreign rascal with my own hand ! ’

So they made him a partner in the plot against Rizzio’s life.

One night the Queen ordered her supper to be served in a tiny room off her bedroom. It was a wild March night, and the little room, hung with tapestries brought from France, would be warmer. This room, and the bigger one where she slept, were in an old tower of the palace. A secret staircase twisted up through the thickness of the walls, with a little door into the supper-room hidden behind the hangings on the wall.

The Queen sat down at the round table, with her Maries about her, and Seigneur Davey standing at the sideboard ready to bring her what she wanted to eat or drink. ‘Leave a seat empty for the King,’ she ordered. She called him King out of politeness, though now she was tired and disgusted with him.

So there was an empty seat at the table. Soon Darnley came in and sat down. Mary still tried to be kind to him and always spoke to him gently. She gave him delicious chicken and some special fruit preserved in syrup. But he seemed nervous and unhappy about something, and she noticed it.

‘Let us have some music,’ she suggested. ‘That will raise our spirits and help us forget the wind outside.’

Indeed the wind was howling about the palace, so that other odd noises could not be heard. Darnley jumped at the

suggestion. Seigneur Davey was delighted too, for he loved singing. He hastily got out some music, propped it up in the middle of the table so that everyone could read it, and then moved one of the candles near the music sheet, to let them see the notes.

The song was an Italian air, sung in parts, and everyone joined in, even Darnley. They were singing away happily, when one of the Maries suddenly clutched her mistress's gown.

'Look!' she cried. 'That curtain moved!'

But Darnley called out hurriedly, 'It's only the wind, or a rat——'

Everyone had stopped singing. They were staring at the curtain which covered the door to the secret staircase. It jerked sideways, and a man stepped into the room– one of the Scots Nobles, wearing full armour, with a naked sword in his hand.

Mary turned at once to her husband. 'Do you know what this means?' she asked.

But the coward Darnley only shrank back in his chair. 'I know nothing,' he muttered.

Mary was brave. She faced the man with the sword in his hand. 'What do you want with me?' she demanded. 'I did not summon you. Leave my presence at once!'

The man stepped farther into the room. Now they could all see the company of other armed Nobles coming up the staircase behind him. 'I want nothing of you, Madam,' said the grim figure before her, 'only this fellow here—' and he pointed his sword straight at the trembling Italian.

Rizzio knew then that they meant to murder him. He ran behind Mary, clutching her skirts and crying 'Justice, Madam, Justice!' And she held out her arms to protect him.

Her women screamed. There was a clank of armour as the rest of the plotters rushed into the tiny room. One of them rudely pushed Mary aside. They dragged the poor little Italian, still screaming for mercy, out of the room and plunged their daggers into him till he lay dead there on the threshold.

Meanwhile Darnley held Mary fast, to prevent her going to help her friend. When the last cries were stilled, and she knew Rizzio was dead, she turned upon Darnley, raging at him.

'Out of my sight!' she cried. 'From now on, I hate you. You are no husband of mine!'

Then she struggled free and ran into the other room to get help. Where were her Maries, her faithful attendants? They had all been hustled away. Even Seigneur Davey's body had gone. And her door into the main part of the palace was locked.

She was a prisoner.

# 4

ALL this had made a good deal of noise. Some of her faithful courtiers, hearing a disturbance, had run to the Queen's rooms, but had found them locked. When they tried to leave the palace to get help from outside, they saw armed guards at all the gates.

But one of the boldest of Mary's supporters, Lord Bothwell, was not going to be baulked by that. He climbed out of a window and ran into the town, calling for help for the Queen.

The people gathered at once, led by their chief magistrate, the Lord Provost. They marched, a great crowd of them, into the courtyard of the palace. All the bells of the city began to ring, though it was late at night. Mary heard the bells ringing, and then she heard shouts of 'The Queen! We want the Queen!' And her heart leaped with joy, for she knew her own people had come to rescue her and were right beneath her windows.

But when she ran forward to speak to them, a man with a sword held her back. 'Say one word, and I'll cut ye into collops!' he hissed. And Darnley was pushed forward to speak to the people instead.

'Good people!' He leaned down and shouted: 'Your

Queen is perfectly safe and happy. The disturbance was only that we had to execute a foreign rascal who was working against the State. I thank you for your loyalty, but we do not need your help.'

The crowd looked up, puzzled for a moment, and then drifted away. After all, Darnley was King, and the Queen's husband too. If he said she was all right, then she must be !

So they all left Mary alone, locked up for the night.

She had time to think then. She must get out of the palace, but how ? The stupidest and weakest of all her enemies was her own husband. Through him, she must make her escape.

Next day, she sent a humble message to him, saying she was sorry for being angry, and would he come and speak to her ? When she got him alone, she seemed gentle and forgiving. But she was not forgiving in her heart ; she only wished to win him to her side.

' Don't you understand,' she said, ' that if I am a prisoner, so are you ? We both sink or swim together. This is a plot to destroy us both. Try to get out of the palace and see ! '

Darnley became frightened. ' What can we do ? ' he stammered.

' Do what I tell you. Go to those Nobles who pretend to be your friends, and tell them I am very ill. Say I am far too weak to try to escape, and it isn't necessary to keep guards at the doors any longer. Then tonight order a great feast, and when they are enjoying themselves, slip away and come to me. We will escape together.'

Darnley did as he was told. His friends called off their guards, and began feasting and drinking. Late that night, Mary and Darnley crept downstairs, out at a side-door to where Darnley had horses waiting in charge of the Captain of the Royal Bodyguard.

The wind had died down and it was bright moonlight.

Mary mounted behind the Captain who set spurs to his horse, and away they went. Darnley galloped off too, but in another direction. Now that the main danger was over, he was afraid his wife's anger would burst out once more. Mary didn't mind. She never wanted to see him again.

She rode all the way to Dunbar Castle. There, in one of the safest of all her fortresses, guarded by the sea outside, she wrote and sent off letters to every part of Scotland, summoning an army to put down the rebels. Sometimes, as she wrote, she looked at Elizabeth's ring on her finger. Supposing no-one rose to help her? Would she have to send that ring to her cousin after all?

But Lord Bothwell, who had climbed out of the window to get help for her, soon got an army together. The rebel Lords did not wait to be attacked. One by one they rode out to Dunbar, humbly begging for pardon. Mary pardoned most of them, because she knew that the one most worthy of punishment was her own husband, and if he escaped punishment, why not they?

But she didn't trust them any more. She went to live in Edinburgh Castle instead of the palace of Holyrood House, because the Castle was built on a rock and well armed with guns, and she felt safe there. And there her baby son was born.

She called him James. She summoned the English Ambassador, and holding the baby out to him said, 'This is the Prince who, I hope, shall first unite the two kingdoms of England and Scotland.'

The Englishman was surprised. 'Why should he succeed before your Majesty and his father ? ' he asked.

Mary sighed. 'Alas ! His father has broken with me.'

Darnley, who was in the room, blushed scarlet. He said reproachfully, 'Is this your promise that you would forgive and forget ? '

Mary looked at him coldly. 'I have forgiven,' she said, 'but I can never forget.'

Darnley left the Castle in a huff. He would not even come back for the baby's christening. He behaved more madly and stupidly than ever, and Mary was glad to let him go. By now she had found someone far stronger than either Darnley or poor Seigneur Davey, to help her with advice.

This was the bold Lord Bothwell. He was a great fighting man, and a good sailor too. She made him Lord High Admiral of Scotland. A ruthless and dangerous man himself, he kept her Nobles in order. They dared not lay a finger on him, or on Mary either, while he was about. She grew to rely on him more and more.

So the country was quiet again. And nobody heeded Darnley now. He was not allowed into the Queen's council chamber. Even the rebel Lords despised him for betraying them. But he was still the Queen's husband. She could not get rid of him, however much she wished to. Some people thought if she could, she would marry Bothwell instead.

Bothwell thought so too. Accustomed to sweeping everyone who hindered him out of his way, he was not going to let a weak boy like Darnley stand in it. Many men he had killed in his time. Was he likely to think twice about Darnley ?

Then news came that Darnley was ill. Perhaps Mary was truly sorry for him. Perhaps she was in the plot too. But, after refusing to have anything to do with him for so long, she went to visit him in the little house just outside Edinburgh where he was slowly getting better. She spoke kindly to him, and helped to nurse him. And Darnley was delighted. He thought that at last she had forgotten as well as forgiven.

They had a friendly supper together, and Darnley was happier than he had been for a long while. Suddenly, however, when it was quite late and dark, Mary jumped up in a hurry.

' I quite forgot ! ' she exclaimed. ' One of my servants was married today and I promised I would dance at her wedding party tonight. I must go back to Edinburgh at once ! '

Darnley was very disappointed. He begged her to stay, but she said she never broke a promise. She kissed him and said goodnight. Then she called for her horse and rode away, leaving him alone.

Presently the lights of the palace went out, and the lights of Darnley's little house went out too, and everyone slept.

At two o'clock in the morning, the noise of a terrible explosion was heard all over Edinburgh. One person said it was like twenty-five big cannon being fired together. Everyone jumped out of bed, and soon the streets were full of hastily dressed people running about and asking each other what had happened.

As soon as it grew light enough, people went out in the direction the explosion had come from, to see what they could find. They found the little house outside the city blown up by gunpowder, and Lord Darnley, the Queen's husband, lying dead in the garden.

# 5

Everyone was sure that Lord Bothwell was the murderer. They even sold his picture in the streets, with '*This is the King's Murderer*' written beneath it. And many people whispered that the Queen must have known the house was to be blown up, or she would not have left it in such a hurry at eleven o'clock that night.

Far away in England, Queen Elizabeth heard what they were saying about her cousin Mary. She sat down and wrote her a letter. After saying how shocked she was at Darnley's death she went on : '*I must tell you boldly that I am far more concerned for you than I am for him. I will not conceal from you that people say you look through your fingers at this deed, instead of avenging it.*'

Elizabeth meant to warn her cousin, but Mary would not be warned. She did not even pretend to keep mourning for her husband, but began to enjoy herself a week after his death. Perhaps it was only great relief that Darnley was out of the way ; perhaps she was too honest to pretend that she still cared for him. And Bothwell was by her side all the time.

He knew very well what people were saying about him, so he demanded a trial. But he rode to the trial with so many soldiers behind him, that the Judges did not dare to find him guilty. Triumphantly he rode through the Edinburgh streets

with his sword drawn, challenging anyone who called him a murderer to fight. But nobody took up the challenge.

A few weeks later, he and Mary Stuart were married.

Faithful Mary Fleming was no longer at hand to warn her :

'Be careful !' She had gone to a home and husband of her own. Only Mary Seton, the pertest and boldest of the four Maries, was left. But even she had sense enough to know that her mistress had done a mad thing in marrying the very man whom everyone believed to have murdered her husband.

The whole of Scotland was shocked. The Scots Lords,

who had been against her anyway, now took their opportunity. One morning, when she looked from the window of the castle where she and Bothwell had gone for their honeymoon, she saw it was surrounded by troops. She was a prisoner again.

She was very brave, and again she escaped. Dressed as a boy, she managed to slip out of the castle and rode away like the wind. Bothwell had escaped first and was rallying the troops that still remained loyal to her.

There they stood, waiting for her orders, on the slope of Carberry Hill outside Edinburgh. And there, opposite, the army which the Scots Lords had gathered together stood grimly waiting. Mary liked danger, and she was a splendid rider. She rode up and down the ranks of her army, encouraging her men. Mary Seton rode at her side as boldly as a boy, with a little red feather in her hat.

But somehow, neither of the armies wanted to move against the other. They were all Scots, and why should they fight each other because their Queen had had too many husbands ?

The French Ambassador had come out to see the fight, and he thought he would make peace between them. So he rode to and fro between the leaders of the armies and brought back to Mary the conditions under which the Scots Lords would promise not to attack.

The chief one was that Bothwell must be sent right away. Now, as soon as Bothwell had safely married the Queen, he had become rough and overbearing to her, so she agreed to this ; but she made the other side promise that they would let him escape safely.

Bothwell took one look at his Queen, and then rode away. She never saw him again. She dismissed her loyal army and went forward to join the Scots Lords, thinking they would give her a safe escort back to her palace in Edinburgh.

But instead, they closed in round her. And though they did escort her back to Edinburgh, it was not to her own palace. They led her right through the streets of Edinburgh, paying no attention to her orders. The common people thronged to see her, as they had done when she was popular and rode in procession accompanied by their cheers.

But this time they did not cheer. ' Murderess ! ' they cried. The roar of their voices filled the streets from end to end, so that Mary grew pale as she rode, her head up, between the Nobles whom she now looked on as traitors.

They locked her up as prisoner in the Provost's own house. Sometimes she flung herself against the windows of the house, calling on passers-by to help her. But they only laughed. Sometimes she sat crouched in a corner of the little dark room, twisting Elizabeth's diamond ring. Should she send it somehow to England, to ask her cousin's help ?

But there was no-one to take it. Anyway, she hated the thought of begging Elizabeth to save her. She was still too proud for that. Surely somebody would rescue her! Where was her half-brother, Lord Moray ? Where were her friends ?

The only one with her was Mary Seton. She was not wise like Mary Fleming or gentle like Mary Livingstone. But she was loyal, and she kept up the Queen's spirits as much as she could.

Suddenly there was a clatter of horses' hooves on the road outside. The two Maries flew to the window. Was it Lord Moray coming to rescue them ? Instead, they saw a number of Protestant Nobles, with a band of soldiers, and two riderless horses being led between them.

The door flew open.

' Come, your Majesty,' a voice said harshly. ' We have found a safer place for you than this.'

Poor Mary had only the clothes she was wearing when they captured her first. This time there was no packing to do. She did not even know where they were taking her. They made her ride a long way into the country, until they came to the shores of a lonely lake where a boat was waiting.

She got down from her horse. The nearest Noble took her hand tightly and led her towards the boat. She could hear Mary Seton scolding angrily behind her, as she was forced to come too. And she could see, away in the middle of the lake, a small lonely island, with the tower of a castle standing against the sky.

' Yes, Madam,' said the Noble who held her hand. ' That is the cage. I don't think your Majesty will escape from it easily ! '

# 6

THE Castle of Lochleven was cold and damp. Day after day, Mary Stuart and Mary Seton looked out on the waste of waters for some sign of a rescue party. They knew now that Lord Moray was not going to do anything for his half-sister after all, because he believed that she had had a hand in Darnley's murder.

'There isn't even a little garden to walk in!' Mary sighed. 'Do you remember our garden on the island long ago?'

'Yes,' Mary Seton answered firmly, 'and I remember that we escaped from that island too.'

They had nothing to do to pass the time, but sewing and embroidery. Mary Stuart embroidered beautifully. She had learned to do so in France. She made a set of embroidered reins for her baby son. She wondered where he was, and how they were treating him. He was so very tiny to be away from his mother.

Far away in England, Queen Elizabeth was moved to pity for her cousin. Forgetting her jealousy, she sat down and wrote an angry letter to the Scots Lords. She told them that if anything happened to Mary Stuart she would do her best

to punish them. And as she was strong enough to march an army into Scotland any minute, perhaps they listened to what she said.

At any rate, Queen Mary was left alone. For months and months she sat embroidering in her prison room, or looking out on the waters of the lake. Soon, though she was sad, she grew calm again. Mary could always make people love her. She won the friendship of all the servants, even of the simple laundress who used to row over to the island once a week to take away the washing and bring it back.

'Have you noticed that the laundress is just the same height as you are ?' Mary Seton said thoughtfully one day.

'Yes, she's very tall, but what about that ?' Mary Stuart replied.

'It gives me an idea,' said the bold Mary Seton.

Next time the laundress came into the room, she took her into a corner and spoke to her urgently, giving her some money.

The woman was as bold as the other, and loved a joke. 'Och, I'll help ye if I can !' she said.

'Quick !' Mary Seton told her mistress, listening at the

door in case they were interrupted. 'Take off your dress and put on hers instead ! Now take this shawl—it's late enough to be cold and damp already. Put it round your head and hold it across your face. Now the laundry basket ! It's heavy, but you must manage to carry it somehow !'

Mary Stuart understood in a flash. She slipped out of her beautiful velvet dress while the laundress tore off her plain woollen one. They dressed in each other's clothes, and Mary tied the laundress's apron round her waist and held the shawl across her face, just as Mary Seton had told her.

The countrywoman stood stiffly, fingering the rich velvet. Mary Seton dragged her over to a dark corner of the room as far away from the window as possible. 'Turn your face away when they come in with our supper,' she whispered, 'and if they don't notice the change, that will give our Queen the whole night to get safely away !'

'I'll do that,' the woman promised, sitting down awkwardly and gathering the rich folds round her feet, 'and I'll bide the consequences too, if it's to help her Majesty. A' they can do is give me a beating. My shoulders are broad enough for that !'

Outside, the corridors were deserted. Other people were in their own rooms, and the servants preparing supper. The Queen-laundress stole along, carrying the heavy washing-basket of soiled linen. Down the back stairs she went, to blunder suddenly into one of the cooks at the bottom.

But the fellow only drew aside, saying ' Eh, Nancy, but ye've a load o' work to tak' home this nicht ! '

Mary muttered an answer through her shawl and fled. The back door of the castle was open. The damp air from the lake came through it but she welcomed it, for it was the air of freedom. There, before her, stretched the little path down to the lake side. The boat was waiting. Soon she would be safe. . . .

The two men from the mainland who rowed the boat back and forward with supplies, were waiting too. They were so accustomed to the laundress, they paid no attention to her. But a young man, a new servant at the castle, was being taken over to the mainland to spend the night there with friends. He had never seen the laundress before. He gazed inquisitively at her as she reached them.

' What passenger is this ? ' he inquired.

' Och, it's just Nancy who does the washin'. Come away and never heed her.'

' Has Nancy a pretty face ? ' the young fellow said teasingly. ' Let's see if she has ! ' And he caught hold of the shawl.

Mary gave a little scream. She put up her hand quickly

to keep the shawl in place. The men stared. Instead of being Nancy's hand, coarse and red and puffed with much washing, it was fine and white and very small. And on one finger there glittered a diamond ring.

' That's no' Nancy ! ' shouted one of the boatmen, pulling the shawl away. ' It's—guid sakes, it's the Queen herself ! '

Mary drew herself up and tried to speak calmly. ' Yes, I am your Queen. I order you to row me over the lake at once ! '

But the servant knew the consequences of that. ' Dinna listen to her ! ' he cried. ' If ye do, we'll all lose our heads ! '

Respectfully, the boatmen took hold of Mary and marched her back to the castle. The laundry basket lay neglected and forgotten on the shore. Mary was crying as they led her to her own room. And the laundress sobbed loudly when she saw that the plot had failed.

' Wheesht noo ! ' said one of the men. ' Ye're a great fool, so ye are, Nancy ! Come away afore onyone else finds it oot. Y'r washin's waiting for ye doon by the lake.'

When they had all left the room again, Mary Seton tried to comfort her mistress by saying : ' At least, Madam, we are no better or worse off than we were before.'

But Mary was gazing down at the ring on her hand. The diamond in it winked up at her like a wicked eye. ' My cousin Elizabeth's ring ! ' she murmured. ' It betrayed me. Will she do the same, I wonder ? '

So the days went on, each exactly like any other. But



C**

Mary managed to make two friends during that weary time. One was Lady Douglas, the wife of the Governor of the Castle, and the other was her son, young George Douglas who acted as page to the Queen.

George Douglas thought he had never seen so lovely or sorrowful a lady in his life. Mary was always thoughtful and sweet to everyone who served her. From being sorry for Mary, George went on to being angry with his father for keeping her prisoner. Day in, day out, he tried to think of a way to help this lovely lady to escape.

A day came when he entered her room to announce : ‘ Visitors for your Majesty ! ’

Visitors ! The two Maries looked at each other wonderingly. Hope suddenly flushed the Queen’s face. ‘ It may be my brother ! ’ she cried. ‘ Perhaps he has come to set me free after all ! ’

But it was not her brother. When George Douglas lifted the heavy curtain to admit the guests, she saw it was two of the Scots Nobles who had taken part against her. One of them carried a long, rolled-up paper in his hand. This he untied and laid on the table before her.

He bowed and said, ‘ We have come from the Lords of the Realm to demand that your Majesty sign this paper.’

‘ What does it say ? ’ She bent over and read it. Then she stepped back from the table, white with rage. ‘ I shall never sign my name to any such thing ! ’ she cried.

The paper called on her to resign the Crown to her baby son, and to give all power of government into the hands of Lord Moray. If she signed it, she would be Queen of Scotland no longer.

The Noble who had put it before her looked very grave. ' If your Majesty refuses, I am to tell you that you will be tried publicly for the death of your husband, Lord Darnley, or at least for knowing about it beforehand. Do you still refuse ? '

' I know nothing about that dreadful murder ! ' she exclaimed hotly. ' And I refuse to stand up in court before all my people and be blamed for something I did not do ! '

They remained silent, looking at her. Then she knew she must sign the paper. She bent over it again, scribbled her name at the foot and tossed it back to the two men. ' You have what you want. But you have made me sign by force, so this does not count. I shall be Queen of Scotland till I die ! '

# 7

It was a public holiday in Scotland, and the bells rang out from every church steeple. Everyone crowded to see the procession of the new king about to be crowned.

A very splendid procession it was. The Nobles and their ladies rode out in their finest robes and jewels. The soldiers marched bravely, with bright flags flying and music playing. Then came the great Lord Morton, carrying the royal Sceptre. After him rode the Earl of Glencairn holding aloft the Sword of State. And then the Earl of Atholl, carrying the golden Crown which Mary had worn, and which Mary Fleming had worn for a night.

Lastly there came the Earl of Mar carrying Mary's little son in his arms. They carried him into church, where John Knox, the great Protestant leader, preached the sermon. And they held the heavy crown over the baby's head and proclaimed him King James the Sixth of Scotland.

And everyone shouted ' God Save the King ! '

At night bonfires were lit all over the country. Mary could see them blazing on the other side of the lake, but nobody seemed to remember her any more. Yet surely there were *some* faithful subjects of hers left ! If she could only reach them and call on them to help her, she felt that she might beat her enemies yet !

Mary Seton, stitching away at her embroidery, thought so too. But she did not see how the escape could be managed. True, there was one way by which Mary Stuart could leave Lochleven, but she feared her mistress would not take it. Still, she could try to persuade her.

' Madam,' she said, ' have you forgotten Queen Elizabeth's ring ? She gave you her promise that she would come to your rescue if ever you sent it back. Don't you think that the time has come now ? '

But Mary Stuart was still too proud. ' That woman pretends to like me,' she answered scornfully, ' but she is not really my friend. I refuse to ask her for anything. Besides, she only wants an excuse to invade Scotland and take it. I won't give her that excuse ! '

Mary Seton sighed. She loved her mistress, but wished she were not so proud. If the Queen did not give way, they might stay here for ever. She felt so despairing, that later, when she was alone with the page, George Douglas, she told him so.

Young Douglas felt it was time for him to do something. For long he, too, had thought and thought about how to set the Queen free. Now an idea had come to him. It was a risky one, and it might not come off. But he and Mary Seton thought it worth trying anyway.

He felt very proud and important as he made all the secret arrangements. He found people living on the other side of the lake who were willing to risk their lives to help the Queen to escape. They promised to have a fast horse ready for her, once she had managed to get out of the castle and cross the lake. And two or three of the boldest offered to have the castle boat manned and ready to fetch her, if a signal was given that she was down on the shore, waiting.

The signal was to be the waving of the Queen's own white veil, and the time was to be at dusk. But meanwhile, young Douglas still had to tackle the greatest difficulty of all. He had to get hold of the castle keys. And since his father, the Governor, never let them out of his sight, how could he manage that ?

At last Douglas thought of a way. It might not succeed but he meant to try it that very night. Every evening the watchers by the shore would be looking out for the signal. The horse with its lady's saddle would be quietly grazing on the opposite side of the lake, ready for its rider. Yes, he would try tonight !

It was a calm evening in early May. The fruit trees beneath Mary's window were covered with blossom as white as her veil. The banqueting hall downstairs, where the Governor dined, was still filled with evening light. The Governor sat down to table with the iron ring of keys flung beside his place.

Douglas, as page, always served the company. The officers and members of the household sat laughing and joking, while the page filled their glasses again and again, with his napkin over one arm. Presently, as if by accident, he dropped the napkin over the keys. Nobody noticed, they were all too busy feasting and drinking. Nor did they notice when, a little while later, the young page picked up his napkin again and left the room, as if to fetch something more for them to enjoy.

But the keys were now inside the napkin, and the napkin was in his hand.

Running like the wind he reached the Queen's room. She stood waiting, warned already and wearing a riding-habit. ' Quick, Madam ! ' he gasped. ' We have only a few seconds before my father notices that the keys are gone ! '

In a flash Mary had run

down the back stairs and slipped out of the door. Douglas locked it after them. 'Run down to the shore,' he ordered her. 'I am going to lock the great door of the main entrance. That will bottle them up!'

With her long skirts held high, Mary ran as fast as she could. The lake waters broke at her feet as she stood there, waving her white veil. Presently she saw, through the dusk, a boat nosing toward her from the castle landing-stage. At the same time she heard behind her a great noise and shouting from the castle itself.

She laughed as she listened. The windows were too high from the ground for anyone to climb out, and the doors were safely locked on the outside. 'A bonny prison indeed!' she exclaimed, for now it held safely her jailers instead of herself.

The boat nosed into the shallows beside her. She stepped into it and was rowed through the darkness across the lake. On the other side were her friends. She was always a splendid rider, and she settled herself in the saddle of the waiting horse and turned its head toward the sea.

# 8

THE news of Mary's escape spread like wildfire all over Scotland.

Many people had wanted to help her, but they had not been able to do so while she was still a prisoner. She went first to Mary Seton's relative, Lord Seton, and from there to another castle, to make her plans and gather her troops together. For now she knew that she must fight her own half-brother Lord Moray, and the Scots Lords who supported him, if she was to be really free and a Queen once more.

Both sides gathered their troops together. Mary's army swelled to six thousand men. But the armies were equal in size and the kingdom was still divided. Some wished her to reign again, while others claimed she had given up her rights to her baby son, and that she was a bad woman anyway, who had probably helped to murder her husband Darnley.

Bothwell was no longer there to fight for her. Whatever his faults, he had at least been a good soldier and full of courage. But he had had to leave Scotland and was wandering somewhere abroad.

The two armies met just outside Glasgow, at a place called Langside. This time neither side hesitated, and nobody made

an offer of peace. Mary's cavalry charged fiercely at once, while Mary herself watched, on horseback, from a little way off.

Lord Moray opened fire and mowed down the horsemen. Then he counter-charged and swept forward, breaking and scattering her troops. Mary could see it happen in the clear light of that morning. She knew she had lost the day; the only thing left was to save herself, and she rode swiftly away.

Night and day she rode, accompanied only by a small

band of faithful friends. She knew her enemies would hunt her down if they could come after her in time. She dared not stop for more than an hour or two's rest and food.

At one halt she scribbled a hasty letter to an uncle of hers in France. 'I have suffered injuries, calumnies, captivity, hunger, cold, heat, flying—without knowing where—ninety-

two miles across the country without once pausing to alight, and then lay on the hard ground, having only sour milk to drink and oatmeal to eat, without bread, passing three nights with the owls.'

At last she reached the very edge of her kingdom. Before her stretched the waters of the Solway Firth and beyond that, England. Here she paused to make up her mind.

If she rode back the way she had come, she would fall into

the hands of the Scots Lords, who would certainly make her a prisoner again, and might even kill her. If she went forward, she would be in a foreign land. That land was ruled by her own cousin, Elizabeth. And Elizabeth had always said she would help her if she were really in need.

Mary was no longer too proud to remind Elizabeth of her promise. She wrote Elizabeth a letter, begging for hospitality—and for clothes, since she had only the riding-habit she wore. And she enclosed Elizabeth's diamond ring.

But a rider would have to bear both the ring and the letter to London, and that would take several days. Mary could not afford to wait where she was, in case her enemies caught up with her. They would not, however, dare to cross the English frontier. Once she herself had crossed it, she would be safe.

So she rode forward again, and passed from one kingdom to the other. The Keeper of a castle outside Carlisle was

amazed to see approaching a little company of riders, and in the middle of them, a tired, dusty-looking young woman almost drooping out of her saddle.

But he was even more astonished when one of the escort of riders rode up to the gate of the castle and shouted, ' Room and shelter for her Majesty, the Queen of Scots ! '

The Keeper knew that the Queen of Scots was the cousin of his own Queen. He hurried to open the gate and make her welcome. Mary was only too glad to be shown a room where she could rest and wait for her cousin's answer.

The only thing that distressed her was the state of her clothes. Unless Elizabeth did what she asked, and sent her new ones, she was going to cut a shabby figure at the English Court !

Poor Mary had always loved fine and beautiful clothes. She could not bear the thought of arriving at Elizabeth's palace without her jewels and velvets. But she was sure Elizabeth would realise that, being a woman herself. Yes, no doubt some fine clothes would arrive along with the invitation to come to London at once !

Meanwhile the horseman carrying her message and the ring was riding as hard as he could from the north of England to the south. He rode through the night as well as through the day, finding fresh horses when he could. And at last, reaching Elizabeth's palace, he handed the letter and the ring to a courtier to give to the Queen.

Elizabeth sat in her library, for she was very fond of books. Her hair looked redder than ever, because now she was older she had begun to dye it, and her face was white and sharp. It did not matter what language a book was written in, because she knew most of them.

She laid down her book and looked round. The courtier who had interrupted her reading, bowed very low, looking frightened. His mistress had a fine temper, and he knew he risked getting the book thrown at him.

'Pardon, your Majesty, but an urgent message has come from the Queen of Scots. She writes from Workington, near Carlisle——'

'What are you saying, fool ? The Queen of Scots would never enter my kingdom without asking permission !'

'From all accounts, Madam, she was allowed no time to ask permission of anyone. Her Lords were in pursuit, and she fled for her life. She casts herself on your Majesty's mercy.'

' Give me the letter ! '

Elizabeth unfolded it roughly. Something fell with a clink into her jewelled and embroidered lap. It was the diamond ring she had sent to Mary, years ago.

She stared at it, then rose to her full height. ' Order my Privy Council to meet at once ! ' she commanded.

One by one her great Statesmen arrived in the Council Chamber. They came, not armed as the Scots Lords had to be, but wearing furred robes, with golden chains round their necks. They did not expect to fight one another because they were peaceable and had no quarrels. And they were both wise and careful.

Elizabeth faced them from her throne-chair at the head of the table. Usually unable to make up her mind, she knew her mind now. All jealousy had been swept away by the piteous appeal in the letter. Mary was her cousin, her blood relation, after all.

' My Lords ! ' she said, in her harsh parrot-voice. ' Our cousin, the Queen of Scots, has arrived in our dominions, asking shelter and protection. We propose to give these to her and to invite her here, as our honoured guest.'

It was not very often that her Statesmen refused to agree with her. But now she saw, with astonishment and anger, that they were silent, looking sideways at one another. After a moment she asked sharply, ' Do you hesitate to agree to my wish ? '

Then the elder Statesman, Lord Cecil, replied. He was the wisest of them all, and Elizabeth trusted him above anyone else.

' Madam,' he said, ' think twice before you receive so dangerous a woman as the Queen of Scots ! She claims to be the next heir to your throne, and she is a Catholic. Once set her at liberty, here in England, and who knows what the Catholics may do ? They may even rally round her and try to put her in your Majesty's place ! '

Elizabeth looked startled. ' I never thought of that ! ' she muttered.

' Then think, Madam, before it is too late. The Catholics make enough conspiracies against your Majesty's rule, and even your Majesty's life. Besides, we are not at war with Scotland. If the Scots choose to reject their Queen, why should we support her ? '

The Queen looked very thoughtful. Then she dismissed the Council. ' I will think over what you have said, and make my decision later,' she said.

For days she paced up and down her room or sat, chin in hand, in the library trying to make up her mind. Every time she glanced down at the diamond ring on her finger, a generous feeling of pity would drive her to her desk, to write an order for the safe convoy of the Queen of Scots toward London.

Besides, she was secretly dying to see with her own eyes this Queen who was actually considered more beautiful and accomplished than herself.

Then Elizabeth would remember Lord Cecil's words. England was mostly Protestant, and she was a Protestant Queen. But the Catholic Party was still very strong. They had always considered Mary should have come to the throne instead of Elizabeth. If Mary were free to meet their leaders and plot with them, who knew what might happen?

And there was that affair of Lord Darnley's death, too. Nobody knew the truth. But people said that Mary had known and approved of his murder. If so, she would not hesitate to approve of her cousin Elizabeth's death, if that would make her Queen of England.

So at last Elizabeth made up her mind. To Mary, anxiously waiting near Carlisle, she sent a very kind letter, together with beautiful clothes and books and everything to make life pleasant. But she did not invite her to London.

Instead, she gave orders that she was to remain where she was.

# 9

SOMETIMES it was in one castle, sometimes in another, but wherever she was taken, and no matter how well she was treated there, Mary Stuart knew that she was a prisoner once more.

Elizabeth did not call it that. She merely wrote suggesting that perhaps her dear cousin might care to be entertained at some fresh place, and see another part of the north of England. A castle was apparently put at her disposal. Elizabeth paid the wages of countless servants and sent her own cook, and her own doctor, to make Mary more comfortable and happy.

But a bird in a cage is never comfortable or happy. No matter what Elizabeth gave her, Mary kept writing and writing to her, begging for the one thing she really wanted. That was her freedom.

A sort of freedom she had. She might ride and hunt as much as she pleased. But always some polite English Lord was beside her, to see that she did not ride too far. She could write to her relations in France, begging them to help her. Elizabeth and Cecil knew the letters could not do any harm, because France was not prepared to go to war with England for the sake of Mary Stuart.

And Elizabeth refused on any account to see her. Perhaps she was afraid to do so. Everyone said that Mary could charm people to do her will. Had not old John Knox said that she drew them to her as a honey-pot draws bees ?

She begged to be allowed to see her little son, but that was not allowed either. When James learned to read and write, he did not even answer his mother's letters, because she addressed them to ' The Prince of Scotland ' and he considered himself King.

The Scots Lords were delighted that Elizabeth had solved the difficulty of what to do with Mary. They felt that they could afford to yield to her wishes in small things, since she could not trouble Scotland any longer. So they had her clothes and jewellery packed up and sent on to her from Edinburgh. And they also said that Mary Seton might join her mistress ; the last of the Maries to stay with her almost to the end.

Perhaps it was Mary Seton who brought the Queen's little dogs with her from Holyrood. Anyway, Mary always had them at her heels, as she had done all her life. Little dogs with coats as smooth as silk, and plumey tails and bright, bulging eyes. She had brought the first ones over from France, and had others sent as they died off.

Now some were rather old, but they still yapped and ran at her heels. ' Don't you remember,' she asked Mary Seton, ' how we used to race them down the long corridors in France ? '

‘ Yes, indeed.’ Mary Seton sighed. And they both saw again the beautiful palace in the midst of the woods ; the long marble corridors, and five little girls running, screaming with laughter, after the dogs.

‘ Pierrot is getting old,’ Mary Stuart said. ‘ I must write to my uncle in France to send me a new puppy. At least he can do that, if he cannot do anything more.’

The new puppy came, with a silkier coat, a plumeyer tail and more bulging eyes than any of them. Mary called him Chou, which really means Cabbage, but is used as a pet-name in France. Chou would not pay the slightest attention to anyone except the Queen. Wherever she moved he moved. Wherever Mary Stuart was to be found, there was Chou.

So time wore on ; summer and winter ; summer and winter. Mary could no longer attempt one of her thrilling escapes, because if she did, who would help her outside ? To the English people she was a foreigner, and the Scots seemed to have cast her off entirely.

Outwardly, she had everything to make her happy, and Elizabeth’s orders were that she was to be treated with the greatest respect, as a Queen. She ate off silver dishes, and had the finest wax candles to light her rooms. Their floors were even covered with carpets, which were very rare and costly in those days. And she had as many as fifty servants to wait on her personally, besides those who did the work of the house. But she had no friend except Mary Seton.

The years went on. Mary's hair was grey now and little Chou began to grow old. Mary was not so pretty as she had been, though still so full of charm that all who came near her loved her. But inside, she was the same desperate, bold, proud woman she had always been. So, when secret messages began to come to her saying the Catholics were ready to rise in her service, she thought that at last a chance had come, not only to be free again, but perhaps to become Queen in Elizabeth's place.

She ought to have remembered that every letter she wrote might be opened and read. She ought not to have answered the letters at all. But Mary Fleming was no longer by her side to whisper 'Be careful!'

She thought she was being very careful indeed, when she sent out and received her plotting letters carefully hidden in a wig, in the sole of a shoe or tucked into the back of a book. She did not know that most of them were discovered by Elizabeth's spies.

There was the plot to raise an army in Holland and bring it over to rescue her. There was the plot to get Spain to attack England in Mary's favour. And the Catholic Nobles of England planned a rebellion, meaning to put Mary upon the throne instead of her Protestant cousin Elizabeth.

But all those plots came to nothing in the end, thanks to the cleverness of Elizabeth's Government. They were all discovered, and those plotters who were caught were put in prison or hanged.

Still Mary wrote busily by the light of her tall wax candles. Still she charmed and won over everyone who came near her, so that they were willing to risk their lives in carrying away her appeals for help. And presently Elizabeth couldn't sleep at night, for wondering what her cousin was plotting next.

Lord Cecil, her wise counsellor, grew frightened and worried too. One day he asked for a private word with Elizabeth. 'Madam,' he said bluntly, 'all this must have an end.'

Elizabeth was looking paler and sharper than ever. All her finery, her satin dress embroidered with gold, her jewellery, could not hide the fact that she was a frightened and worried woman.

'What end?' she demanded.

'The end of Mary Stuart, or of your Majesty. So long as

HODGSON

that woman lives, there will always be people who will try to kill you, so as to put her in your place.'

Elizabeth shivered a little. 'She is a crowned Queen,' she muttered, 'and she is my cousin as well. If I agree to her death, what will the world say?'

'One kingdom cannot contain two Queens,' Cecil replied. 'Your Majesty has had plenty of proof that so long as the Queen of Scots lives, your own life is in danger.'

'She has never plotted against my life, so why should I take hers?'

'She may still do so. And then it will be too late.'

Elizabeth snapped her feather fan open and shut, frowning. Presently she said: 'Bring me proof that my cousin the Queen of Scots has actually plotted against my life. Then I will sign any order you wish. Until that happens, leave her alone.'

But the great Lord Cecil was not satisfied yet.

'She has too much liberty to plot and receive her friends. Let me change the Governor who has charge of her. She will be kept more strictly by the man I choose. He will prevent her from endangering your Majesty's life, and thus she may prolong her own.'

That seemed reasonable enough. Elizabeth nodded, feeling relieved that any blame for treating Mary Stuart badly would belong to the new Governor, and not to her.

# 10

Now there were no more fine wax candles. No more silver plate or soft carpets, and no more riding or hunting expeditions in the fresh air.

Mary's new Governor was a hard man, upon whom her charm and beauty made no impression at all. Her faithful friend Mary Seton had been sent away to a convent in France. Her other servants were dismissed, so that she had no-one to help her smuggle her letters outside of her prison. As the Governor was a strict Protestant, she was even forbidden to see her priest.

Instead of a great castle or manor house, she was given two little rooms in a tumbledown building. For exercise she could walk about in a small yard into which the sun never shone. Yet she would not give in. She continued to call herself Queen of Scotland.

'Am I not still a Queen?' she whispered into the long silky ear of her old spaniel, Chou. 'And have I not escaped from other prisons besides this?'

Yes, but she needed more than one small faithful dog to help her. Outside her prison there was a young man who was ready to do so. Anthony Babington was a member of an

old Catholic family. Mary had been in prison now for nineteen years. He had heard of the beautiful prisoner since he was a little boy. Often he would ride his horse as near to her castle as he dared, hoping to catch a glimpse of the Queen who had come through so many strange adventures.

Now, when he heard how badly the Governor had begun to treat Mary he blazed with indignation. He screwed up his courage and wrote a letter to her. He said that if she only gave the word, he was prepared, for her sake, to kill Elizabeth and set her free.

He managed to smuggle the letter in to Mary somehow. But she was too wise to reply. So he wrote again. And this time, perhaps, she was not so wise. . . .

Queen Elizabeth had scarcely risen and been dressed by her maids when a page came to tell her that the great Lord Cecil wanted to speak to her immediately. So she tapped her way on her high-heeled shoes, down the long corridor of her palace, to where Cecil stood waiting.

He had a letter in his hand.

'Madam,' he said, 'is this letter in the handwriting of your Majesty's cousin, the Queen of Scots?'

She glanced at it and said: 'It seems so.'

'My spies took it from the messenger who was conveying it to a foolish young man, Anthony Babington. This Babington had offered to kill your Majesty, and as you see, the Queen of Scots has written agreeing to the plot.'

Queen Elizabeth snatched at the letter and read it. She had grown very pale. 'You were right, Cecil,' she said as she handed it back, 'the thing must have an end.'

When Mary heard that the letter had been found, and that she was supposed to have written it, she exclaimed indignantly that she had done nothing of the sort. True, the handwriting looked like hers, but handwriting could be copied. She knew that her cousin Elizabeth wanted to get rid of her. Someone had arranged this, so as to give her a good excuse.

*Had* she written the letter? Nobody knows.

But one day a little while after, three high officers of State arrived at the Castle of Fotheringay where Mary was now imprisoned. They called her into their presence, and the chief of them read the Death Warrant, signed by Elizabeth's own hand.

Mary drew herself up proudly. Only once in her life had she shown fear, after seeing her troops routed at the Battle of Langside. She would never show fear again. Placing her hand on a Bible on the table near her, she swore : 'I have never either desired the death of the Queen or endeavoured to bring it about, or that of any other person.'

Was she speaking the truth ? Nobody knows.

They told her she was to die the next morning. When morning came she got up very early, because she meant to dress more carefully and more magnificently than for any State Ball in France or Scotland. She took two hours to dress, and she chose to wear a gown of black velvet stamped with gold. Under it she wore a crimson silk petticoat. Her dress had a long train, and she fastened over her hair a fine white veil which fell right down over the train.

Lastly, as she turned to leave her room, she picked up an ivory crucifix and carried it in her hand. She meant to die like a Queen, and a Catholic Queen.

On the threshold, an old servant of hers knelt down and kissed her hand. 'This is the saddest day of my life,' he said, 'for I go back to Scotland to tell them that the Queen is dead.'

'No, don't tell them that,' she said ; 'tell them that today Mary Stuart has seen the last of her troubles.'

They had draped the great hall of Fotheringay with black. Two masked executioners stood waiting. They begged her forgiveness for what they must do. ‘ I forgive you, and thank you too,’ she said, ‘ and I hope to die like a true Scot, and a true Frenchwoman.’

Then, without the slightest sign of fear, she laid her head on the block. The next moment the axe had fallen. The true story of Mary Stuart had come to an end at last. But when they ran to pick up her body, out from her velvet skirts ran her last loyal friend, the old spaniel Chou. Growling and barking, he would not allow anyone to touch his mistress. They had to pick him up first and take him away, before they dared to touch Mary.

Within the hour a messenger had started for London on horseback, with the news that Elizabeth's chief enemy was dead. If anyone expected her to be pleased, however, they were mistaken.

Elizabeth had changed her mind twenty times since signing the Order for Mary's death. Now she stormed and raged at the unfortunate messenger, and her temper was such that nobody dared come near her. Yet, the night after she heard the news, her attendants noticed that their Queen had her first good sleep for months.

Time went on, and Elizabeth grew to be an old woman. She never spoke about Mary, but sometimes she twisted a diamond ring on her finger, and then her face grew sad and thoughtful.

Since she had never married, and had no children to come after her, everyone wondered whom she would make her heir. And one day a courtier was bold enough to ask her.

The old Queen looked at him in surprise. ‘ Who but my cousin in Scotland ? ’ she said. And by that, perhaps, she was trying to make amends.

So Mary's son, James the Sixth of Scotland, became in time James the First of England, and the two Crowns were joined : the great Crown of England, now kept in the Tower of London ; and the Crown of pale gold set with Scots pearls which you can see in Edinburgh Castle today ; that very Crown once worn by Mary Fleming when she played at being Queen for a night, and by Mary Stuart.